This book belongs to ...

....

OXFORD
UNIVERSITY PRESS

Great Clarendon Street, Oxford, OX2 6DP,
United Kingdom

Oxford University Press is a department of the University of Oxford.
It furthers the University's objective of excellence in research, scholarship,
and education by publishing worldwide. Oxford is a registered trade mark of
Oxford University Press in the UK and in certain other countries

ISBN: 978-0-19-273432-7

1 3 5 7 9 10 8 6 4 2

Typeset in Edbaskerville

Paper used in the production of this book is a natural, recyclable product made
from wood grown in sustainable forests. The manufacturing process conforms
to the environmental regulations of the country of origin.

Acknowledgements;
Series Editors: Kate Ruttle, Annemarie Young

READ WITH
Biff,
Chip &
Kipper

I Can Trick a Tiger
and Other Stories

OXFORD
UNIVERSITY PRESS

Tips for Reading Together

Children learn best when reading is fun.

- Talk about the title and the picture on page 7.
- Identify the letter pattern *ng* in the title and talk about the sound it makes when you read it.
- Look at the *ng* and *ck* words on page 8. Say the sounds in each word and then say the word (e.g. *s-i-ng, sing; sh-o-ck, shock*).
- Read the story and find the words with *ng* and *ck*.
- Talk about the story and do the fun activities at the end of the book.

Children enjoy re-reading stories and this helps to build their confidence.

Have fun!

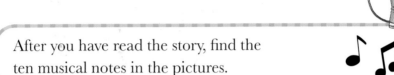

After you have read the story, find the ten musical notes in the pictures.

The main sound practised in this book is 'ng' as in *sang*. The other sound practised is 'ck' as in *rock*.

For more hints and tips on helping your child become a successful and enthusiastic reader look at our website www.oxfordowl.co.uk.

The Sing Song

Written by Roderick Hunt
Illustrations by Nick Schon, based on
the original characters created by
Roderick Hunt and Alex Brychta

OXFORD
UNIVERSITY PRESS

Read these words

sing   song

ding   long

along   sang

rock   shock

"It is a Sing Song," said Dad.

"Let's go to the Sing Song,"
said Dad.

10

"Yes, let's go along to it," said Mum.

They went to the Sing Song.

They met Wilf and Wilma.

Wilf and Wilma sang a song.
They had fun singing it.

Kipper had a song to sing.

Mum sang it with him.

Biff and Chip sang a song.

It was a sad song.

Dad sang a song.

It went on and on.

Dad sang and sang.

23

Dad won the Sing Song.

Talk about the story

Who did the family meet at the Sing Song?

What song did Kipper sing?

Why were Biff and Chip surprised that Dad won?

What do you like to sing?

25

Spot the difference

Find the five differences in the two pictures of Dad.

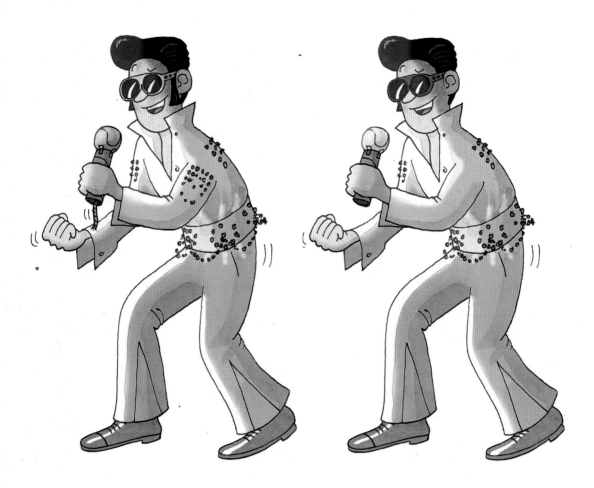

Tips for Reading Together

Children learn best when reading is fun.

- Talk about the title and the picture on page 29.
- Identify the letter pattern *ck* in the title and talk about the sound it makes when you read it.
- Look at the *ck* and *oy* words on page 30. Say the sounds in each word and then say the word (e.g. *r-o-ck-e-t*, *rocket*; *b-oy*, *boy*).
- Read the story then find the words with *ck* and *oy*.
- Talk about the story and do the fun activity at the end of the book.

Children enjoy re-reading stories and this helps to build their confidence.

Have fun!

After you have read the story, find the five mice hidden in the pictures.

The main sound practised in this book is 'ck' as in *back*.
The other sound practised is 'oy' as in *toy*.

For more hints and tips on helping your child become a successful and enthusiastic reader look at our website www.oxfordowl.co.uk.

The Backpack

Written by Roderick Hunt
Illustrated by Alex Brychta

OXFORD
UNIVERSITY PRESS

Read these words

toy backpack

ducks rocket

pocket boy

luck pick

Chip was in a toy shop.

He put his backpack
by the ducks.

A boy put his backpack
by the ducks.

"Look at this rocket,"
said Chip.

"My cash is in my backpack," he said.

In the zip pocket.

Mum got a backpack.

But it was not Chip's backpack.

The boy had Chip's backpack.

Pick it up, Nick.

Chip had the boy's backpack.

Chip was upset.

That boy has my cash.

"Let's get it back," said Mum.

Mum and Chip ran ...

... to this shop ...

… to that shop.

The boy got on a bus.

"Stop that bus," said Mum.

The bus did stop.

Chip got his backpack back.

Talk about the story

Where did Chip put his backpack?

Where was Chip's cash?

Why did the boy pick up Chip's backpack?

What have you lost and where did you find it?

A maze

Help Chip get to his backpack.

Tips for Reading Together

Children learn best when reading is fun.

- Talk about the title and the picture on page 51.

- Look through the pictures together and discuss what you think the story might be about.

- Read the story together, pointing to each word and inviting your child to join in.

- Give lots of praise as your child reads with you, and help them when necessary.

- Enjoy re-reading the story and encourage your child to say the repeated phrases with you.

Children enjoy re-reading stories and this helps to build their confidence.

Have fun!

After you have read the story, find the cat hidden in every picture.

This book includes these useful common words:
said   looks   put   stop

For more hints and tips on helping your child become a successful and enthusiastic reader look at our website www.oxfordowl.co.uk.

Super Dad

Written by Roderick Hunt
Illustrated by Alex Brychta

OXFORD
UNIVERSITY PRESS

"Look at Dad," said Mum.

"Dad looks silly," said Wilma.

"No, he looks good," said
Wilf.

Dad put on a red nose.

"Oh no!" said Wilma.

"Dad looks so silly."

Dad had a bucket.

"Put your coins in here,"
he said.

Oh no! A man took Dad's
bucket.

"Stop!" called Mum. "Come
back."

But the man did not stop.

Dad got on a bike.

The man ran fast . . .

but Dad was faster.

"Got you," said Dad.

"Help!" said the man.

"Super Dad!" said Wilma.

Talk about the story

Why did Wilma say that Dad looked silly?

What happened after the man took the bucket?

How did Dad stop the thief?

What would you like to dress up as?

A maze

Help Dad to catch the thief.

Tips for Reading Together

Children learn best when reading is fun.

- Talk about the title and the picture on page 73.

- Look through the pictures together and discuss what you think the story might be about.

- Read the story together, pointing to each word and inviting your child to join in.

- Give lots of praise as your child reads with you, and help them when necessary.

- Enjoy re-reading the story and encourage your child to say the repeated phrases with you.

Children enjoy re-reading stories and this helps to build their confidence.

Have fun!

After you have read the story, find the tree frog hidden in every picture.

This book includes these useful common words:
look said you out

For more hints and tips on helping your child become a successful and enthusiastic reader look at our website www.oxfordowl.co.uk.

I Can Trick a Tiger

Written by Cynthia Rider,
based on the original characters
created by Roderick Hunt and Alex Brychta
Illustrated by Alex Brychta

OXFORD
UNIVERSITY PRESS

Floppy was dreaming.
He was in the jungle.

A tiger jumped out.
"Got you!" he said.

"I can trick a tiger,"
said Floppy.

"Look out!" said Floppy.

"There is a bee on your nose."

"Oh no!" said the tiger,
and he let Floppy go.

A crocodile jumped out.
"Got you!" she said.

"I can trick a crocodile,"
said Floppy.

"Look out!" said Floppy.

"There is a bee on your nose."

"Oh no!" said the crocodile,
and she let Floppy go.

A snake slid out.

"Got you!" she said.

"I can trick a snake,"
said Floppy.

"Look out!" said Floppy.
"There is a bee on your nose."

"Oh no!" said the snake,
and she let Floppy go.

A rabbit jumped out.
"Got you!" said Floppy.

"Look out!" said the rabbit.
"There is a bee on your nose."

Buzzzzzzzz!

"Oh no!" said Floppy.

Talk about the story

Why did the tiger let Floppy go?

What would you do if you had a bee on your nose?

How do you think Floppy felt when the bee landed on his nose?

Have you ever played a trick on anybody? Was it a funny trick?

Rhyming words

Match the things that rhyme.

Read with Biff, Chip and Kipper
The UK's best-selling home reading series

Phonics

First Stories

	Phonics	First Stories	
Level 1 Getting ready to read			
Level 2 Starting to read			
Level 3 Becoming a reader			
Level 4 Developing as a reader			
Level 5 Building confidence in reading			
Level 6 Reading with confidence			

Phonics stories help children practise their sounds and letters, as they learn to do in school.

First Stories have been specially written to provide practice in reading everyday language.

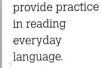

Read with Biff, Chip and Kipper Collections:

2 Phonics and 2 First Stories in every collection

Phonics support

Flashcards are a really fun way to practise phonics and build reading skills. **Age 3+**

My Phonics Kit is designed to support you and your child as you practise phonics together at home. It includes stickers, workbooks, interactive eBooks, support for parents and more! **Age 5+**

Read Write Inc. Phonics: A range of fun rhyming stories to support decoding skills. **Age 4+**

Songbirds Phonics: Lively and engaging phonics stories from Children's Laureate, Julia Donaldson. **Age 4+**

Help your child's reading with essential tips, advice on phonics and free eBooks
www.oxfordowl.co.uk